Jack's hair

Written by
Dot Meharry

Illustrated by
Hannah Wood

Jack didn't like his hair. It stood straight up. Every morning, Jack tried to smooth it down with water, but when it dried, it just stood up again.

"Look at my hair," cried Jack. "Why won't it stay down?"

"Your hair looks fine as it is," said his mother.

"No, it doesn't," said Jack. "I look like a rooster."

At school, Jack's teacher was talking about genes. She told the class that children often inherit their looks from their parents.

At home that night, Jack said, "My teacher says that we get our looks from our parents, but your hair doesn't stick up like mine."

"Our hair is about the same colour though," said Dad. "I use hair gel on mine. You could try some."

After dinner, Jack's dad gave him some
hair gel. Jack rubbed the gel on his hands.
He smoothed his hair down, and it did stick
to his head.

But Jack did not like the gel in his hair because
it made it feel slimy and greasy.

The next time Jack went to the hair salon for a haircut, he asked the hairdresser what he could do with his hair.

"You have nice hair, Jack," said the hairdresser. "It looks fine as it is, but I'll put some hairspray on it when I'm finished. That will keep your hair flat."

But Jack didn't like how the hairspray smelled.

One Sunday, Jack's family had a visitor.
"Come and meet my cousin, Jim,"
said Jack's dad.

Jack had never met his dad's cousin before.
The two looked at each other and smiled.
Jim pointed to his head. His hair stood
straight up too.

"Your hair stands up like mine," cried Jack.

"That's right!," said Jim. "When I was your age I thought I looked just like a rooster."

"That's what I think!" said Jack.

Jim had brought some old photographs with him.
The family looked at them. Jack picked one up.

"Who's this?" he asked.

"That's your great-grandad when he was a boy,"
said Jim.

"His hair stands up too," said Jack.

Everyone looked at the photo and laughed.

"That's where our hair comes from," said Jim. "It's in our genes!"

"We've been learning about genes at school," said Jack. "This is cool. I'll have to show my teacher this."

"I have an idea," said Jim. "We could copy the pictures and make a chart with them."

Jack and Jim sorted through the photos.

They made a family-tree chart.

They stuck all the photos

with sticking-up hair

on to the chart.

The next day when Jack went to school, he let his hair stand up. He took his chart to school to show his teacher.

"These are wonderful family pictures, Jack," she said. "This chart shows just what we've been talking about in class."

All the children gathered round to look
at Jack's chart.

"Your family has great hair," they laughed,
and Jack laughed too!

Tadpole trouble

Written by
Frances Bacon

Illustrated by
Jennifer Cooper

Last summer, Grandma came to stay.

She arrived in her little yellow car.

In the back of the car was a big jar.

In the jar were twenty tadpoles.

"Oh dear!" said Mum
and Dad. "Tadpoles
might mean trouble!"

"Tadpoles! What fun!" I said.

I got a tank and put some plants and water in it. Then I put the tadpoles in the tank.

I kept the tank in my room. Every day I fed my tadpoles. I liked to watch them eat and swim.

Soon the tadpoles began to change.
They grew some legs. Their tails
got smaller, and their bodies got bigger.
I made a chart about my tadpoles.

My Tadpole Chart

Frog

Eggs

Tadpole
1 week

12 weeks

9 weeks

6 weeks

Then, one night... **PLOP!** Something wet was on my head. I turned on the light.

There were little frogs all over my room. They jumped on my bed. They leaped on my bedside table. They hopped all over the floor.

"Mum, Dad, come quickly!" I cried.

Dad opened my bedroom door.

"Oh no!" he shouted. "We were right.
The tadpoles have turned into trouble!"

The frogs jumped past Dad and hopped
down the hall. Soon there were frogs
everywhere.

Mum, Dad and I chased
the frogs high and low.
We chased those leaping
frogs until we caught
them all.

The next morning, we took the frogs
to a nearby pond. We set them free.

"Goodbye, frogs," I said, as the frogs
jumped and splashed in the water.
"The frogs like their new home."

This summer, Mum, Dad and I
went to visit Grandma. We went in
our big red car. We took a big jar.
In the jar were twenty tadpoles.

"Oh dear!"
said Grandma.
"I hope we don't
have tadpole trouble!"

Ideas for Parents

- Reading with children is an important way of encouraging a love of books. It familiarises your child with the patterns of the written language and helps increase his or her vocabulary, assisting him or her on the road to literacy.

- Urge your child to join in with reading. Encourage him or her to finish sentences, try new words and read sections on his or her own. Always read the book a number of times. Repetition familiarises children with language patterns and makes it more likely that they will join in.

- Children learn best when an experience is enjoyable, so always make reading together a positive and fun experience.

Helping Children to Understand the Text and Build Reading Skills

Jack's Hair

- Talk about the colour and type of hair in your family. Discuss the meaning of the word *inherit*.

- Discuss all the things Jack did to try to smooth his hair down. As you read together, ask questions that encourage your child to predict what might happen next.

- You and your child could look at photos of your family and make a family tree together.

Tadpole Trouble

- Enjoy the illustrations as you read the book together.

- Encourage your child to use the illustrations to predict what is going to happen in the story.

- Ask questions as you read, such as: *Why do you think Mum and Dad said, "Tadpoles might mean trouble"? What do you think will happen next?*

- Discuss how the story ends. Ask: *Is this a good ending? Why?*